"Good morning my princess, it's time to rise and shine."

"Mommy do I have to? I don't want to get up."

"Monique it's your first day of school with big kids, you should be excited."

"No, mom. I'm scared I'm too little to be around big kids."

"Okay, Monique," Momma said. "We can talk more about this over breakfast."

"Mom, you made me waffles," said Monique excitedly, "my favorite! You are the best mom in the world."

"Monique grab your lunch off the counter and meet me in the car. Make sure you don't let Blue out," reminded Momma.

"Today I am going to be a leader," Monique tells herself. "I'm going to make sure that I don't let anyone make me do anything I don't want to do, whether they want to be my friend or not."

"Have a good day at school and remember to always be a person with integrity," Momma advised.

"What does integrity mean mom?" asked Monique.

Momma replied, "It's doing the right thing when nobody's looking, being a person that others can trust. So always be honest even when you think you're going to get in trouble. "

"Okay mom," Monique replied. "I have to go before the bell rings."

"I love you, Monique," Momma said. "Have a good day and don't worry, you will be fine. I will be in front after school."

"Good Morning, Ms. Turner," said Monique as she greeted her teacher. "Do we have assigned seats or can we sit any-where?"
Monique look for the table that has your name on it, that's your assigned seat, "replied her teacher. "Once everyone is in their seats, we will all introduce ourselves."

"Hi, my name is Monique"
"Hi, I'm Tiffany"
"Hi, I'm Butter"
"Hi, I'm Beans"
"It's nice to meet each of you," Monique says. "I was so scared to come to school, but now I'm happy to be here."

"Good morning students," said Ms. Turner with a
very warm and friendly smile. "I would like someone
to come to the front of the class and tell us what
they think it means to be a good person."

"Monique, would you like to come up and share your answers with us?" asked Ms. Turner.

"Yes ma'am," replied Monique. "My mom always tells me to be a good person and be a person with integrity."

"That's awesome Monique," congratulated Ms. Turner. "Can you tell the class what integrity means.?"

It means your honest and always do the right thing even when nobody's watching.," shared Monique"

"Very well said, Monique."

"My mom always tells me to treat people with respect if I want to be respected," said Tiffany.
Butter adds to the conversations by sharing, "My mom always tells me to respect my elders."
"My mom tells me to always spread love and kindness," Beans said.

Ms. Turner was very pleased with what her students shared. She then told them, "I want each of you to know that you're very special, you can be anything you want to be. People in the world will doubt you, judge you, and sometimes they will hurt your feelings. Everything that happens has a purpose to it, we just have to figure out what it is and not take it personally."

"Ms. Turner my mom always says when you take it personally you can make things worse.,' Monique says.
"Monique your mom has been teaching you right," confirms Ms, Turner. "I love how outspoken you are."
 Now the school day is about to come to a close, Ms. Turner tells her students, "Ok class, the bell is about to ring, please gather your things."

Tiffany, would you like to be my new friend?
Yes, I'm happy I was able to make a new friend on the 1st day of school.
We will be friends forever as long as we never betray each other.
 Tiffany that will never happen as long as we both always show integrity and never take it personally.

Just like she said, Momma was waiting for Monique outside the schoolhouse. "How was school today?" she asked.

"It was great mom," Monique shared. "I even met a new friend. I told the whole class what integrity means today, my teacher was impressed that I knew what that word meant."

"I knew you would do great in school, " said Momma. "We are so proud of you."

As Monique and Momma got home Monique began to think about all the wonderful things that happened that day. Before she went upstairs to wash up for dinner she shared, "Mom, I can't wait to see what happens at school tomorrow."

Hello Reader, My name is Monique. I hope you enjoyed reading all about my first day of school. I now know how important that day was because it was the beginning of new friendships, new interests, and a lot of new memories. On the next few pages, I want you to write all about your first day of school. You can write about anything you want. If you don't want to write about your first day, you can write about any other day or even make up a story of your story.

Whatever you choose to write about I want to encourage you to always act with integrity and remember that whatever happens to you, you will be able to move past it and be better because of it as long as you remember:

ITS NEVER PERSONAL, ITS ALWAYS PURPOSE.

Title of your story: _____

Will you continue your story or write a new one? What exciting things did you experience during your first day of school?

One of the best things about going to school is that we learn something new almost everyday. What are some of the things that you've learned?

Made in the USA
Middletown, DE
04 May 2022